*Unless the L*ORD *builds the house,*
those who build it labor in vain.

—PSALM 127:1

The Art of Marriage® Connect Series

Building Your Marriage to Last
Improving Communication in Your Marriage
Building Teamwork in Your Marriage
Enjoying Your Marriage in the Second Half

Coming in Fall 2014

Resolving Conflict in Your Marriage eBook
Mastering Money in Your Marriage eBook
Growing Together in Christ
Building Up Your Spouse
Managing Pressure in Your Marriage

welcome to the
art of marriage connect

Marriage should be enjoyed, not endured. It is meant to be a vibrant relationship between two people who love each other with passion, commitment, understanding, and grace. So secure is the bond God desires between a husband and a wife that he uses it to illustrate the magnitude of Christ's love for the church (Ephesians 5:25–33).

Do you have that kind of love in your marriage?

Relationships often fade over time as people drift apart—but only if the relationship is left unattended. We have a choice in the matter; our marriages don't have to grow dull. Perhaps we just need to give them some attention.

That's the purpose behind the Art of Marriage® Connect (AOMC) Series—to provide you a way to give your marriage the attention it needs and deserves. This small-group study is biblically based because, in the Bible, God has given the design for building a loving and secure marriage. His plan enables a man and a woman to grow together in a mutually satisfying relationship and then to reach out to others with the love of Christ. Ignoring God's plan may lead to isolation and, in far too many cases, the breakup of the home.

Whether your marriage needs a complete makeover or just a few small adjustments, we encourage you to consult God's design. Although written thousands of years ago, the Bible still speaks clearly and powerfully about the conflicts and challenges men and women face.

Do we really need to be part of a group? Couldn't we just go through this study as a couple?

While you could work through the study as a couple, you would miss the opportunity to connect with friends and to learn from one another's experiences. You will find that the questions in each session not only help you grow closer to your spouse, but they also create an environment of warmth and fellowship with other couples as you study together.

What does it take to lead an AOMC group?

Leading a group is much easier than you may think, because the leader is simply a facilitator who guides the participants through the discussion questions. You are not teaching the material but are helping the couples discover and apply biblical truths. The special dynamic of an AOMC group is that couples teach themselves.

The study guide you're holding has all the information and guidance you need to participate in or lead an AOMC group. You'll find leader's notes in the back of the guide.

What is the typical schedule?

Most studies in the Art of Marriage Connect Series are six to eight weeks long, indicated by the number of sessions in the guide. The sessions are designed to take sixty minutes in the group with a project for the couples to complete between sessions.

Isn't it risky to talk about your marriage in a group?

The group setting should be enjoyable and informative—and nonthreatening. THREE SIMPLE GROUND RULES will help ensure that everyone feels comfortable and gets the most out of the experience:

1. Don't share anything that will embarrass your spouse.
2. You may pass on any question you do not want to answer.
3. If possible, complete the couple's project between group sessions.

What other help does FamilyLife® offer?

Our list of marriage and family resources continues to grow. Visit FamilyLife.com to learn more about our

- Weekend to Remember® marriage getaway, The Art of Marriage®, Stepping Up®,FamilyLife Blended™, and other live conferences and hosted events;
- slate of radio broadcasts, including the nationally syndicated *FamilyLife Today®*, *Real FamilyLife® with Dennis Rainey*, and *FamilyLife This Week®*;
- multimedia resources for small groups, churches, and community networking;
- interactive products for parents, couples, blended families, small-group leaders, and one-to-one mentors; and
- blogs, forums, and other online connections.

about the author

Dennis Rainey is the president and cofounder of FamilyLife (a ministry of Cru) and a graduate of Dallas Theological Seminary. For more than thirty-five years, he has been speaking and writing on marriage and family issues. Since 1976, he has overseen the development of FamilyLife's numerous outreaches, including the popular Weekend to Remember marriage getaway. He is also the daily host of the nationally syndicated radio program *FamilyLife Today*. He and his wife, Barbara, have six children and numerous grandchildren.

contents

on building your marriage to last

When a man and woman are married, they stand before witnesses and proclaim their commitment to a lifetime of love. They recite a sacred vow "to have and to hold . . . from this day forward . . . to love, honor, and cherish . . . for better, for worse . . . for richer, for poorer . . . in sickness and in health . . . as long as we both shall live."

It's a happy day, perhaps the happiest in their lives. And yet, once the honeymoon ends, once the emotions of courtship and engagement subside, many couples realize that falling in love and building a good marriage are two different things. Keeping those vows is much more difficult than they thought it would be. They have not prepared for the long haul. Couples that would not think of buying a car, investing money, or even going to the grocery store without some preparation, enter into marriage with no plan for how to make their relationship succeed.

In this study you will discover the biblical plan and tools that God makes available to husbands and wives. The plan is reliable, and the tools never wear out; they are not man-made. May you find great hope and long-lasting joy in using them to build your marriage.

—Dennis & Barbara Rainey

~1~
Preventing Isolation

Guarding our hearts from selfishness is essential to a healthy and God-honoring marriage.

warm-up

Introduce yourselves as a couple by telling the group one of the following things about your relationship (talk briefly with each other to decide what to share):

- When and where you met
- One fun or unique date before you were married
- One humorous or romantic time from your early married life
- Your favorite Christmas, birthday, or anniversary memory as a couple

Enjoy meeting new friends in your group and getting to know more about those you already know.

Picture This

Coin Toss: Use this exercise as a fun way to kick off the study and to help illustrate the issue of selfishness.

Dig out all the coins you can find in your pocket or purse and put them in a pile between you and your spouse. Then take turns flipping coins—ladies first. If a coin comes up heads, the wife gets to choose a coin to keep; if it's tails, the husband gets to pick. Do this for a couple of minutes. Then gather with the other couples and answer this question: What thoughts went through your mind as you decided which coins to keep?

master designs

Most people would choose to keep the coins of greatest value. While this was a harmless game, we recognize that selfishness is natural to all of us and is harmful to marriage. Left unchecked, selfishness can cause couples to pull away from each other into isolation. In this session we will discuss ways to guard our marriages from the effects of selfishness.

Intimacy: Choose It or Lose It

1. During the engagement period and early marriage, many couples seem to experience a high level of romance and emotional closeness. But as time goes by, they sometimes feel more distant. Why do you think this happens?

2. One of the main reasons people get married is to find intimacy—a close, personal relationship with another person. Yet many couples discover that intimacy does not come naturally. Why do you think this is?

3. Read Isaiah 53:6. What do you see that helps explain the challenge to achieving intimacy in our marriages?

4. What are some ways that selfishness exhibits itself in marriage?

Suggestion: Speak respectfully of your spouse. When you're sharing an illustration about something that went wrong in your marriage, be sure the issue has been resolved and your spouse agrees to your sharing it with others.

Moving Toward Togetherness

5. Selfishness in a marriage will cause a couple to drift apart from each other, leading eventually to isolation. How does isolation affect a marriage?

6. Why do you think some people are willing to tolerate isolation instead of working to build oneness in their marriage?

7. Read Mark 10:35–45, and see how Jesus dealt with a selfish request. What help for your marriage can you find in Jesus' response?

8. Read Philippians 2:3–4. What are some proven ways to defeat selfishness and overcome isolation, according to this passage?

9. What have you heard in this session that can help you build greater intimacy in your marriage?

keystone principle
To build intimacy, be alert to the needs
of your spouse and work to meet those needs
before seeking to fulfill your own.

make a date

Set a time for you and your spouse to complete the couple's project together before the next group meeting.

....
date

....
time

....
location

Scan this code for additional content.

Or visit FamilyLife.com.

couple's project

On Your Own

Answer the following questions:

1. When have you felt especially close to your spouse?

2. What contributed to that closeness?

3. When has selfishness detracted from your closeness?

4. What would your marriage be like if you lived unselfishly? What changes would this require of you?

5. Knowing that the opposite of selfishness is self-denial and generosity, what can you do for your spouse or give up for your spouse during the next week? (For example, give up normal Saturday activities to do something with or for him or her.)

6. Read 1 Peter 3:8–12. Based on this passage, what are some things you should do when you believe your spouse is being selfish?

With Your Spouse

1. Take a few minutes to talk with each other about your day by answering these questions:

   • What was the best thing that happened to you today?

   • What was the worst thing that happened?

   • What was the funniest thing that happened?

2. Share your discoveries from the six questions you answered on your own.

3. No one enjoys hearing that he or she is being selfish. Your marriage can benefit if you know how to best approach your spouse when you believe he or she is being selfish. Share a couple of ways you would like your spouse to help you deal with selfishness.

4. Together read the story Jesus told in Matthew 7:24–27, and discuss how you can relate this parable to building your marriage.

5. Close your date by praying for each other.

Remember to take your calendar to the next session for Make a Date.

~2~
Developing Oneness

Oneness begins when both husband and wife build their marriage from the same set of designs: the Bible.

warm-up

Dream House

Individually, take two or three minutes to sketch a floor plan of your dream house. After you are finished, get with your spouse to compare floor plans and answer the following questions:

> Each person will need a sheet of paper for this exercise.

- In what ways are our floor plans similar?

- What are the biggest differences?

After each couple has had time to compare floor plans, invite the group to discuss some ways that this exercise illustrates marriage. For example, what challenges are you likely to encounter if you build from different plans?

Project Report

If you completed the couple's project from the first session, share one thing you learned.

master designs

In the first session we looked at how selfishness can cause couples to drift apart and into isolation. In this session let's look at the Bible to learn about God's plan for replacing isolation with oneness.

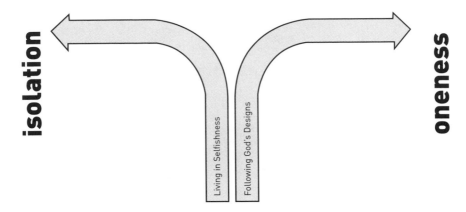

isolation ← Living in Selfishness | Following God's Designs → **oneness**

Living in selfishness leads to isolation, while following God's designs leads to oneness.

Benefits of Oneness

1. Read Psalm 133:1 and Ecclesiastes 4:9–12. What do these scriptures say are some of the benefits of oneness in a relationship?

Suggestion: If you have a large group, you may want to break into smaller groups of about six people to answer the Master Designs questions. After finishing each section, take time for subgroups to share their answers with the whole group.

2. From your experience what are some other benefits of being "one" with your spouse?

Achieving Oneness

3. What would society say are some ways to build oneness in marriage?

4. What do you think is missing from most secular instruction about achieving oneness?

5. Read Philippians 2:1–4. Paul addresses the issue of oneness among Christians. How can you apply these principles to your marriage?

6. Describe a time when you and your spouse were not of one mind on an issue. What was the result?

God's Purposes for Marriage

7. Have each couple choose one of the following verses. (It's okay for the same verse to be selected more than once if more than three couples are in the group.)

- Genesis 1:27
- Genesis 1:28
- Genesis 2:18

Read your verse, and share with the group how you think it relates to God's purposes for marriage.

keystone principle
To achieve oneness, you must share a strong commitment to God's purpose for marriage.

8. How well does your marriage reflect God's image and model His attributes to others? As a couple give yourselves a rating from 1 (low) to 10 (high) in the areas and relationships that follow. Also jot down some ways you can demonstrate these traits.

We reflect God's . . .	to each other	to our families	to others
. . . perfect love for imperfect people			
. . . loving-kindness by serving to meet needs			
. . . commitment by patient support			
. . . peace by resolving conflicts			

Evaluate with your spouse the areas in which you were strongest and those that need the most improvement. What steps can you take to better reflect God's image and model His attributes in your marriage?

9. Share with the group something you really appreciate about your spouse. After everyone has spoken, go around the group a second time if you would like. Then take prayer requests, and close with a time of prayer.

make a date

Set a time for you and your spouse to complete the couple's project together before the next group meeting.

....
date

....
time

....
location

Scan this code for additional content.

Or visit FamilyLife.com.

couple's project

On Your Own

Take about twenty minutes to answer the following five questions.

1. What is the purpose of your marriage?

2. In what aspects of oneness is your marriage succeeding?

3. What aspects of oneness need work in your marriage?

4. On a scale of 1 (low) to 10 (high), how like-minded are you and your spouse on the values and goals of your marriage?

5. What are some things you can do to promote oneness in your marriage?

With Your Spouse

1. Discuss your answers to the five questions above.

2. Agree on any action steps you should take and how you will implement them.

3. Pray together for each other and for your success in following God's designs for marriage.

Remember to take your calendar to the next session for Make a Date.

~3~

Receiving Your Spouse

Oneness in marriage requires receiving your spouse as God's perfect provision for your needs.

warm-up

I know you are, but what am I?

In each of the following six categories, how do you see yourself? How do you see your spouse? How does your spouse see you? On the spectrum lines for each category, place a *Y* where you see yourself and an *S* where you see your spouse.

When you're finished, compare your results with your spouse's. Then share with the group the category in which your ratings most agreed or most disagreed.

MUSIC
A little bit country ———————————————— A little bit rock and roll

MOVIES
Comedy ———————————————— Drama

NUTRITION
Health food ———————————————— Junk food

FINANCES
"You can't take it with you." ———————————————— "A penny saved is a penny earned."

VACATION
Go, go, go ———————————————— Slow down, relax

TECHNOLOGY
Wired ———————————————— Off-line

Project Report

Share one thing you learned from the couple's project from last session.

master designs

We've seen that selfishness produces isolation in marriage, and following God's designs leads to oneness. Now let's discuss the importance of receiving your spouse as God's special gift to you.

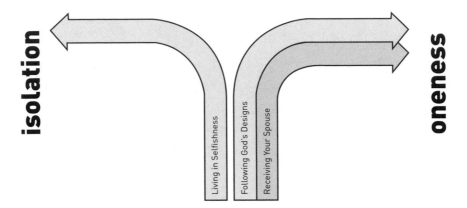

Receiving your spouse as God's gift to you helps create oneness in marriage.

In Genesis 2:18–24 we find the story of the creation of Eve. Let's look at what we can learn from this passage to help us fully accept our spouse as God's provision.

Our Need for a Spouse

1. Read Genesis 2:18–20. What need did God build into Adam? Would you agree or disagree that God gave you the same need?

God's Provision for Our Need

2. Read Genesis 2:21–22. How did God go about creating Eve? Be specific.

3. Why do you suppose God chose to create Eve the way He did?

Our Response to God's Provision

4. Read Genesis 2:23–24. How do you think Adam felt when he first saw Eve?

5. How were Adam and Eve able to recognize they were made for each other?

keystone principle

You can fully accept your spouse because God is aware of your need and is trustworthy to meet it.

You and Your Spouse

6. In what ways does modern culture encourage you to be overly independent of your spouse?

7. What are some things that cause people to reject rather than accept their spouses?

Picture This

Reciprocity: Use common household tools to illustrate the need for couples to accept each other and to value their differences.

Each couple should have a common household tool that has two similar yet opposing parts (like scissors, tweezers, pliers, manual can opener). Take a minute to study the tools and to comment on your observations about what each is designed to do, how it works, what makes it unique, etc. Then discuss with your group what these tools illustrate about marriage and the purpose in spouses accepting each other.

---

8. Consider the results of not receiving your spouse. What have you observed in the relationships of married couples who do not accept each other as God's provision for their needs?

9. If you truly receive your spouse as God's provision for you, how can that affect your attitude toward your spouse's weaknesses?

10. What are some ways you need your spouse? What are some differences in your spouse that God uses to complement you?

> Answer question 10 with your spouse. After answering, you may want to share an appropriate insight or discovery with the group.

keystone principle

A God-honoring marriage is not created by finding a flawless spouse but by allowing God's perfect love and acceptance to flow through an imperfect person (you) toward another imperfect person (your spouse).

make a date

Set a time for you and your spouse to complete the couple's project together before the next group meeting.

....
date

....
time

....
location

Scan this code for additional content.

Or visit FamilyLife.com.

couple's project

On Your Own

Write a love letter to your spouse, using the questions under "Love Letter" to prompt your thoughts. Before starting your letter, spend five or ten minutes in prayer with the following points as a guide.

Prayer time

1. Have you in any way rejected, withdrawn from, or held bitterness toward your spouse? If so, admit it to God, confess it as sin, and thank Him for His forgiveness.

    If we confess our sins, he is faithful and just to forgive us our sins and to cleanse us from all unrighteousness. (1 John 1:9)

2. Commit to God, by faith, to receive your spouse based upon the fact that God is trustworthy.

3. Commit to God to trust Him with your spouse's weaknesses and to love your spouse unconditionally, putting no demands on your spouse to have to "earn" your acceptance.

Love Letter

Write the answers to the following questions in the form of a letter.

1. What qualities most attracted me to you when we first met?

2. What qualities do I most appreciate about you now that we're married?

3. How have our differences helped me grow spiritually and emotionally?

4. What steps will I commit to take to love God and you more?

With Your Spouse

1. Exchange letters. (You may want to read the letter you receive aloud, or your spouse may want to read his or her letter to you.)

2. Discuss what you learned from the letters.

3. Tell your spouse about the commitments you made to God during your prayer time.

4. Pray together. Take turns thanking God for each other.

Remember to take your calendar to the next session for Make a Date.

~4~

Securing the Relationship

Building a strong and lasting marriage involves leaving parents, uniting with each other, and becoming one.

warm-up

Answer one of the following two questions:

1. What experience have you gone through together that has drawn you closer to each other?

2. What was one of the first challenges to your commitment to each other that you faced in your marriage?

Project Report

Share with the group something that you found significant in doing the "Love Letter" assignment from last session.

master designs

In the last session we looked at how we can receive our spouse as God's provision for our needs. In this session we will discuss what it takes to secure our marriage relationship.

The plan for securing a God-honoring marriage has three practical phases, found in one short verse in Genesis:

Therefore a man shall leave his father and his mother and hold fast to his wife, and they shall become one flesh (2:24).

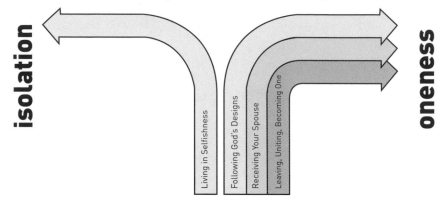

God's design for oneness includes the process of leaving, uniting, and becoming one.

A common error in marriage relationships is the assumption that these phases have already been completed. Many people think the command to leave parents, hold fast, and become one flesh is only for newlyweds. This session will show how each phase involves lifelong growth in openness and trust.

Phase One: Leaving
Case Study

Craig was happy with their new home until he received some startling news after they moved in. Karen's parents, who lived in the same town, had decided to sell the home they had owned for twenty-five years and move to a house across the street! Karen seemed thrilled. Craig was not. He thought Karen's mother had a controlling personality, but Karen had a difficult time understanding his concern.

Read the case study aloud, choosing a different reader for each of the three parts. After reading, answer the questions that follow.

Karen: They were lonely in that old house. Now we can see them more often, and Mom can help with the kids.

Narrator: After several years of apartment living, Craig and Karen bought their first home. And it happened just in time—their second child was due only two months after the closing date. Their purchase was a beautiful four-bedroom home in a new subdivision. The price had been a little beyond their means, but both Craig's parents and Karen's parents had given them some money to use toward the down payment.

Craig: But you see them almost every day anyway! You know how much I like your parents, but we have to have a life of our own. With them here it will be like they're still in charge of our lives. Your mom will be over here telling us how to raise our kids.

Karen: Mom does nothing but help us week after week. Just last weekend you didn't have any problem with her babysitting our son while we went on a date.

Craig: Yes, and for fifteen minutes I also had to listen to her tell me all the things I'm doing wrong with Tommy. You'd think she never made any mistakes when she was our age.

Karen: She's a parent, Craig. They can't stop giving advice just because we've left home. We'll be doing the same thing when we're older. Besides, I don't see you speaking up when your father pressures us to spend Christmas with them every year.

Craig: That's totally different.

Karen: No, it's not. You say we need to live our own lives. Have you told your parents that? Have you stood up to them when they try to manipulate us and make us feel guilty just because we want to start our own traditions for the holidays?

Craig: You know how hard it is to stand up to my dad.

Karen: Yes, I do. And that's my point. If we're going to talk about living our own lives, let's step back and look at everything—not just my parents.

1. What are some of the mistakes the people in this story are making?

2. What do you think Craig and Karen's next steps should be?

3. What happens in a marriage relationship when

   - parents are too clingy?

   - spouses depend more on parents than each other?

4. Ephesians 6:2 says, "Honor your father and mother." What are some ways that you can establish independence from your parents while still honoring them?

Phase Two: Uniting

5. In Genesis 2:24 what does "hold fast to his wife" mean? What is the relationship between leaving your parents and holding fast to your spouse?

6. What factors in marriage and in our culture can make it difficult to remain united and committed to your spouse over a lifetime?

Phase Three: Becoming One

7. The third phase in securing a God-honoring marriage is to "become one flesh"—to establish physical intimacy. Why is becoming one flesh important in achieving oneness in marriage?

8. Write down two or three of the most romantic times you've had with your spouse. Share these with the group if you can, or be sure to share them with your spouse later.

keystone principle

The foundation of a God-honoring marriage is established as you leave, unite, and become one.

The Result: Naked and Unashamed

9. Genesis 2:25 tells us, "And the man and his wife were both naked and were not ashamed." What is the significance of this? How does this demonstrate oneness?

make a date

Set a time for you and your spouse to complete the couple's project together before the next group meeting.

....
date

....
time

....
location

Scan this code for additional content.

Or visit FamilyLife.com.

couple's project

As a couple, plan a special date. Talk about a place you would like to go or something you would like to do. Discuss things you could do to make this date romantic. To help generate some ideas, you may want to think back to some previous special times and recall what made those occasions memorable.

On Your Own

1. Use the following chart to rank yourself in each area of leaving your parents.

1. No dependence on parents
2. Little dependence on parents
3. Some dependence on parents
4. Strong dependence on parents
5. Total dependence on parents

1	2	3	4	5	Financial Dependence
1	2	3	4	5	Social Dependence
1	2	3	4	5	Emotional Dependence
1	2	3	4	5	Acceptance and Approval

2. What area of "leaving parents" do you need to work on most? What are some ways you can do this?

3. Answer the following questions either *Y* (yes) or *N* (no).

    Y N   I have not threatened to leave my spouse within the past two years.

    Y N   My spouse is secure in my commitment to our marriage.

    Y N   I am more committed to my spouse than to my career.

    Y N   My spouse knows I am more committed to our marriage than to my career.

    Y N   I am more committed to my spouse than to my friends and hobbies.

    Y N   I don't withdraw emotionally from my spouse for an extended period of time following a conflict.

    Y N   I generally do not leave my spouse mentally by staying preoccupied with other things.

    Y N   I am interested in my spouse's needs and actively do what I can to meet them.

4. Review your answers, and determine some ways you can demonstrate a stronger commitment to your spouse.

5. If this exercise has pointed out some specific areas where you need to ask your spouse's forgiveness, list them.

6. What setting makes it easy for you to share intimately with your spouse?

7. How could the two of you improve the intimacy you share?

8. What do you most enjoy about your sex life?

9. In what ways, other than physical, are you one with your spouse?

With Your Spouse

1. Review the "Leaving" exercise, and share your answers to question 2. Discuss ways you can support each other in this.

2. Share your answers to questions 4 and 5 regarding "Leaving" and "Uniting."

3. Share with each other your answers to the "Becoming One" questions (7–8).

4. Work together to identify one or two actions to take in the coming week in response to your discussion.

5. End your date by praying together.

Remember to take your calendar to the next session for Make a Date.

~5~
Fitting Together

Husbands and wives have been given biblical responsibilities that complete rather than compete. When embraced, these lead to greater trust, peace, and security in marriage.

warm-up

Cultural Confusion

1. In our culture many voices are telling men and women how they should live. According to the culture, how should men live in order to be successful in their marriages? What are these voices telling women?

2. In what ways have marital roles changed during the last few decades? How have these changes strengthened marriages? How have they weakened marriages?

Project Report

Share one discovery you made from last session's couple's project.

For this session we recommend dividing into two groups—one for husbands and one for wives. If you prefer to keep them together, see page 100 of the leader's notes for suggestions.

master designs

Oneness increases as a couple follows God's designs together, receives each other as God's gift, and then secures their relationship by leaving parents, uniting with each other, and becoming one. In this session we will discuss the biblical responsibilities that are essential to husbands and wives fitting together so that love increases.

Only as a husband and wife understand the unique roles God has given them can they enjoy the oneness he intended in their marriage.

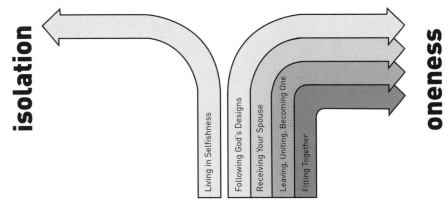

isolation | oneness

Living in Selfishness | Following God's Designs | Receiving Your Spouse | Leaving, Uniting, Becoming One | Fitting Together

A part of oneness involves fitting together—fulfilling your biblical responsibilities as husbands and wives.

For Husbands

The husband's first responsibility: becoming a servant-leader

1. How is a husband's position as leader illustrated in Ephesians 5:23?

2. Leadership as described in the Bible is quite different from what we often see in our culture. What insights do you gain about leadership from Mark 10:42–45?

3. How would becoming a servant-leader change a man who

    • tends to be passive and does not accept his responsibilities?

    • is dictatorial, refuses to listen to his wife, and demands submission from her?

The biblical concept of the husband assuming responsibility for leadership in marriage and a wife submitting to that leadership is one of the most difficult to understand and therefore to fulfill. It is important to recognize that leadership and submission work in marriage only when a husband and wife are committed to following Christ with total humility.

keystone principle

A husband who is becoming a servant-leader is one who is in the process of denying himself daily for his wife.

The husband's second responsibility: unselfish loving

4. Read Ephesians 5:25–27. What does it mean for a husband to love his wife as Christ loves the church?

5. How would this kind of love, this denial of self, communicate love to your wife?

6. Read how God describes the demonstration of love in these passages:

   - John 15:13
   - 1 Corinthians 13:4–7
   - Philippians 2:3–4

   Which of these demonstrations of love does your wife need most? How can you show that love to her?

keystone principle
The husband who is becoming an unselfish lover
will put his wife's needs above his own.

The husband's third responsibility: caring

7. What does Ephesians 5:28–30 add to your view of your responsibility to your wife?

8. *Nourish* means to foster growth, to make growth easier. What does your wife need from you to help her grow?

> In the same way husbands should love their wives as their own bodies. He who loves his wife loves himself. For no one ever hated his own flesh, but nourishes and cherishes it, just as Christ does the church, because we are members of his body. (Ephesians 5:28–30)

9. The term *cherish* is from the Greek word meaning "to keep warm" or "to take care of" and indicates esteeming someone as a priority. How can you show your wife you esteem and value her? Be specific.

10. Based on what you have studied and discussed, write a biblical job description for a husband and then share it with the group.

keystone principle

*The husband who is becoming the caring leader
of his home encourages his wife to grow and
become all that God intends her to be.*

For Wives

The wife's first responsibility: making your marriage a priority

11. Read Proverbs 31:27. What does it mean for a wife to "look well to" or to "watch over" the ways of her household?

12. Consider what happens to your marriage when you do or do not "look well to" your relationship with your husband. Complete the following statements.

    When I keep our relationship a priority, I would describe our marriage as:

    When I do not keep our relationship a priority, I would describe our marriage as:

13. What are the biggest obstacles you face in keeping your marriage a priority?

keystone principle

Becoming an excellent wife requires that a woman keep her relationship with her husband second only to her relationship with God.

The wife's second responsibility: unselfish love

14. The apostle Paul wrote that older women should "train the young women to love their husbands and children" (Titus 2:4). Why do you think this training is so important?

15. In our culture love is generally equated with a feeling. We need to look at Scripture to find the full definition of love. What insights do you gain about love from the following passages?

    • John 15:13

    • 1 Corinthians 13:4–7

    • Philippians 2:3–4

keystone principle

*The wife who is becoming an unselfish lover will
put her husband's needs above her own.*

The wife's third responsibility: submission

16. Read the following passages:

    - Ephesians 5:22–24
    - Titus 2:3–5
    - 1 Peter 3:1–6

    What reactions does the idea of submission in marriage generate
    among women today? What do you think causes those reactions?

17. Does the idea of submission challenge you? Why or why not?

18. Read Ephesians 5:25–33. What additional insights does this pas-
    sage give about the roles of husbands and wives?

19. Ephesians 5:33 speaks of the importance of the wife respecting her husband. How can you show respect to your husband?

keystone principle

In order for a husband to successfully lead, he needs a wife who will lovingly submit to his leadership.

make a date

Set a time for you and your spouse to complete the couple's project together before the next group meeting.

....
date

....
time

....
location

Scan this code for additional content.

Or visit FamilyLife.com.

couple's project

On Your Own

Take a moment to pray. Ask God to show you how you can be the best possible husband or wife. Then ask yourself the following questions.

1. In general how do I feel about the roles God has given my spouse and me in our marriage relationship?

2. In what ways has this session challenged the way I think about our responsibilities in marriage?

3. In practical ways how can I demonstrate servant-leadership to my wife, or how can I support my husband in his desire to lead our family biblically?

4. Is there anything I could *give up* to show love to my wife? How can I express my needs to my husband so he will know that I am supportive of him?

5. What is a responsibility my spouse fills that I really appreciate? How can I show appreciation for this?

With Your Spouse

1. Share and discuss your answers to the previous questions.

2. From your discussion, describe one insight you have gained about your spouse.

3. What are some specific ways you can support and encourage each other as you carry out your roles as husband and wife?

4. Close your date by praying together. Thank God for each other, and ask for His help in meeting the commitments you've made.

Remember to take your calendar to the next session for Make a Date.

~6~

Building in the Spirit

A husband and wife can experience true oneness only as they live by faith, in the power of the Holy Spirit.

warm-up

The Moral of the Story

Think back to the childhood tale of "The Three Little Pigs." What is the moral of the story? Now read Jesus' story of the wise and foolish builders (Matthew 7:24–27).

- What is similar in the two stories? What is the key difference in the conclusion of the stories?

- In marriage, what are some of the foundations on which people build?

- On what foundation does a wise couple build?

Picture This

Bouncing Balloons: This exercise illustrates the need for help in living out a God-honoring marriage. Each person will need an uninflated balloon and a marker.

Pass around balloons and markers until everyone has an uninflated balloon and a marker. Blow up and tie your balloon, then write on your balloon some of the practical things you have learned during the past five sessions. Once everyone's balloons are ready, toss them into the air in the middle of the group. As a group try to keep all the balloons in the air for as long as you can. You may want to keep time to see how long you can make it. Try this more than once to see if you can improve on your time. When you've finished, pick up the balloon closest to you, and answer these questions:

- What does the balloon you are holding say?
- How easy was it to keep all the balloons up?
- How easy is it to do everything you know you should do in your marriage? Why?

Project Report

Share one thing you learned from the couple's project from last session.

master designs

For a home to meet the demands and to weather the storms of life, its builder must be God. Jesus said it was to our advantage that He go to the Father because He would send God's Holy Spirit (the "Helper" or "Comforter," the Third Person of the Trinity) to lead us, to show us His ways, and to empower us to represent Him to the world (see John 14:26). As two people build a relationship with each other, it is essential that they both yield to the Holy Spirit and allow Him to lead them in every facet of their marriage.

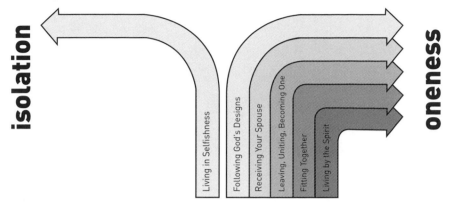

isolation

oneness

Living in Selfishness

Following God's Designs

Receiving Your Spouse

Leaving, Uniting, Becoming One

Fitting Together

Living by the Spirit

In order to be fully one, a husband and wife should each commit to live by the Spirit.

The House That Human Nature Builds

1. Read Romans 7:18–19. Why do you think it is a struggle at times to do the right thing?

2. Read Galatians 5:16–21. What effects can your own desires and effort ("the works of the flesh") have on your marriage relationship?

The House the Spirit Builds

3. You have read "the works of the flesh" (Galatians 5:19–21); now look at "the fruit of the Spirit." Read Galatians 5:22–26. What are the characteristics of a person who is living by the Spirit?

4. Why do you think it is important for us to yield to the Holy Spirit and depend on His power in marriage?

5. What specific fruit of the Spirit mentioned in verses 22 and 23 do you see most evident in the life of your spouse?

6. What specific fruit of the Spirit do you need more of to improve the oneness in your marriage? Explain.

The Holy Spirit in Your Life

7. The Holy Spirit plays many roles in the life of a Christian. Each couple should choose one of the passages that follow. (It's okay for a couple to take more than one passage or for more than one couple to have the same passage.)

   - John 14:26
   - John 16:8
   - John 16:13
   - Acts 1:8
   - Romans 8:16
   - Romans 8:26

   Read your passage, and discuss the work of the Holy Spirit that it reveals. Take turns sharing with the group your verse and its insight into the ministry of the Holy Spirit.

8. In what ways can the Holy Spirit help you build your marriage?

   If you would like the power of the Holy Spirit in your life and your marriage, give control of your life to Christ. Confess your sins, and let Christ take over. To live consistently in the power of the Holy Spirit, you need to make certain that you are living daily under God's control.

keystone principle
*Only through the Holy Spirit can you
build a God-honoring home.*

9. End the session with a time of prayer. Say the following prayer if it reflects the desire of your heart:

Dear God, I need You. I acknowledge that I have been in control of my life and that, as a result, I have sinned against You. I thank You that You have forgiven my sins through Christ's death on the cross for me. I now ask You to take control of my life. Empower and guide me through Your Holy Spirit. As an expression of my faith, I now thank You for taking control of my life through the Holy Spirit. I pray this in Jesus' name, amen.

keystone principle

The home built by God requires both you and your spouse to give control of your lives to the Holy Spirit.

make a date

Set a time for you and your spouse to complete the couple's project together before the next group meeting.

....
date

....
time

....
location

Scan this code for additional content.

Or visit FamilyLife.com.

couple's project

On Your Own

Answer the following questions:

1. What is one insight you have gained about the Holy Spirit from this session?

2. In what ways does the Holy Spirit help you in your life?

3. On a scale of 1 (low) to 10 (high), how much control over your life do you feel the Holy Spirit has?

4. Where in your life do you need the power of the Holy Spirit the most right now?

5. What in your life might be hindering the work of the Holy Spirit?

6. Confess to God any sin that might be hindering His work in your life, and ask Him to help you walk in the Spirit.

With Your Spouse

Share your spiritual journey by answering the following questions:

1. Who has had the greatest spiritual impact on you? In what way?

2. Choose one Bible story, passage, or verse that means a lot to you and explain why.

3. Share your answers from the time you spent alone with God. Your relationship will benefit from openly discussing spiritual things—as well as from confiding questions or struggles you may have. (Caution: Be forgiving if your spouse reveals a disconcerting struggle.)

4. How can you help and encourage each other to walk in the power of the Holy Spirit?

5. In what practical, everyday situations could the power of the Holy Spirit make a difference in your marriage?

6. Close your time together by praying for each other.

For God's Eyes Only

An exercise that many Christians have found meaningful is to take a sheet of paper and spend time alone with God, asking Him to reveal any sin that is unconfessed before Him. The following steps are recommended:

1. Title the page "For God's Eyes Only." Prayerfully list on the page actions and attitudes in your life that are contrary to God's Word and purposes. Focus on areas that affect your spouse.
2. After a time of self-examination, write the words of 1 John 1:9 across your list of sins, thanking God for His absolute forgiveness of all that you have done in the past and will do in the future.
3. Thank Him for sending His Son to the cross to die for your sin.
4. It may be necessary and appropriate for you also to confess to your spouse any attitudes or actions that have been harmful to him or her. Caution: If you are unsure about the appropriateness of sharing something, seek wise counsel.
5. Destroy the page.
6. Bow in prayer, and acknowledge God's authority over your life.

Remember to take your calendar to the next session for Make a Date.

~7~

Shaping Your Legacy

The influence of your marriage will outlive you. What will the coming generations know about God because of your legacy?

warm-up

Lasting Legacy

Our lives have been shaped by the influence of others. Look over the following list of skills and think about who taught you each skill. Pick one thing from the list and share with the group who taught you the skill. You may also want to tell about some other important thing this person passed on to you.

- Tie shoelaces
- Say "please" and "thank you"
- Throw a ball
- Bait a fish hook
- Pray
- Work
- Drive a car
- Be a good sport
- Cook
- Read

Project Report

Share one insight or discovery from last session's couple's project.

master designs

You have studied that oneness with God and your spouse is necessary for overcoming isolation in marriage. This oneness you are establishing in your home also enables you to reach out to others.

God's heart of love virtually breaks over people who have not yet received His forgiveness through His Son, Jesus Christ. God desires to reconcile every individual to Himself (2 Peter 3:9). You and your spouse and those you influence for Christ, including your children and stepchildren, are all a part of God's purpose.

Married people who work together to meet needs beyond their own front door will leave a spiritual legacy that will outlive them. The legacy will ultimately be different for everyone. The true test in leaving a God-honoring legacy is an individual's or a couple's faithful fulfillment of God's mission through the stewardship of time, talents, and treasure. A God-honoring legacy can be partially measured by the character of the descendants who have been spiritually influenced by a person's life.

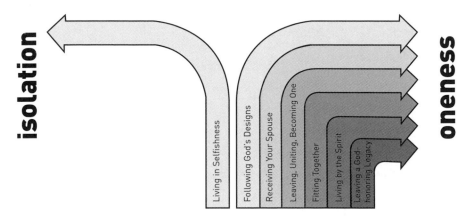

The oneness you establish as a couple allows you to impact others in a God-honoring way with your lives.

Understanding Our Legacy

1. When you think of a heritage or a legacy, what comes to mind?

2. What kind of legacy did your parents leave you? How do you feel about this legacy?

3. What are some other types of legacies people leave? List as many different kinds as you can.

keystone principle
The legacy you received is not as important as the legacy you will leave.

4. What do the following scriptures tell us about the type of legacy God desires us to leave?

    - Joshua 24:14–15

    - Psalm 112:1–2

    - Proverbs 22:6

    - 2 Timothy 1:5

    - 3 John 4

Leaving a Legacy Beyond Yourself

5. What do Matthew 28:19–20 and 2 Timothy 2:2 say about leaving a spiritual legacy?

6. According to Deuteronomy 6:4–9, how do you leave a God-honoring legacy with your children?

7. What would your legacy be if it were based on your life only through today?

keystone principle

The legacy you leave is determined by the influence you have on your physical and spiritual descendants.

8. What do you want your legacy to be?

9. What people might God want you to influence?

10. As you come to the end of this study, take some time to reflect as a group on what you have experienced. Pick one of the following questions to answer and to share with the group.

   • What has this group meant to you during the course of this study? Be specific.

- What is the most valuable thing you discovered?

- What would you like to see happen next for this group?

- How have you changed?

make a date

Set a time for you and your spouse to complete the last couple's project of the study.

....
date

....
time

....
location

Scan this code for additional content.

Or visit FamilyLife.com.

couple's project

On Your Own

1. Write a description of the legacy you desire to leave

    - to your family descendants;

    - to your spiritual descendants—those you lead to Christ and disciple.

2. What is one major objective you wish to accomplish this year to help you

    - leave a God-honoring line of family descendants?

    - leave a God-honoring line of spiritual descendants?

With Your Spouse

1. Think back to the first meeting of this study. How did you feel? What expectations did you have? How did your experience compare with your expectations?

2. Describe something from this study that has helped your marriage.

3. Identify something you learned about your spouse.

4. What has been the best part of this study for you?

5. Compare the legacy descriptions you wrote. Then write a common description of the legacy you both desire to leave:

   • For your family descendants

- For your spiritual descendants

(You may want to copy or type this description and place it somewhere at home or work as a reminder.)

6. What is one specific action you can agree to take together to help your marriage leave a God-honoring legacy? (For some ideas see page 67.)

7. Beyond this study what can you do as a couple to continue regularly setting time aside to build your marriage?

8. Close with a time of prayer, thanking God for each other and for your marriage—what He has done and will do!

where do you go from here?

We hope that you have benefited from this study in the Art of Marriage Connect Series and that your marriage will continue to grow as you both submit your lives to Jesus Christ and build according to His designs. We also hope that you will reach out to strengthen other marriages in your local church and community. Your influence is needed.

A favorite World War II story illustrates this point clearly.

The year was 1940. The French army had just collapsed under Hitler's onslaught. The Dutch had folded, overwhelmed by the Nazi regime. The Belgians had surrendered. And the British army was trapped on the coast of France in the channel port of Dunkirk.

Two hundred and twenty thousand of Britain's finest young men seemed doomed to die, turning the English Channel red with their blood. The Fuehrer's troops, only miles away in the hills of France, didn't realize how close to victory they actually were.

Any attempt at rescue seemed futile in the time remaining. A thin British navy—the professionals—told King George VI that they could save 17,000 troops at best. The House of Commons was warned to prepare for "hard and heavy tidings."

Politicians were paralyzed. The king was powerless. And the Allies could only watch as spectators from a distance. Then, as the doom of the British army seemed imminent, a strange fleet appeared on the horizon of the English Channel—the wildest assortment of boats perhaps ever assembled in history: trawlers, tugs, scows, fishing sloops, lifeboats, pleasure craft, smacks and coasters, sailboats, even the London fire-brigade flotilla, ships manned by civilian volunteers—English fathers joining in the rescue of Britain's exhausted, bleeding sons.

William Manchester writes in his epic novel, *The Last Lion*, that what happened in 1940 at Dunkirk seems like a miracle. Not only were most of the British soldiers rescued, but 118,000 other Allied troops as well.

Today, the Christian home is much like those troops at Dunkirk—pressured, trapped, demoralized, and in need of help. The Christian community may be much like England—waiting for professionals to step in and save the family. But the problem is much too large for them to solve alone.

We need an all-out effort by men and women "sailing" to rescue the exhausted and wounded families. We need an outreach effort by common couples with faith in an uncommon God. For too long, married couples within the church have abdicated to those in full-time vocational ministry the privilege and responsibility of influencing others.

We challenge you to invest your lives in others, to join in the rescue. You and other couples around the world can team together to build thousands of marriages and families and, in doing so, continue to strengthen your own.

Be a HomeBuilder

Looking for more ways to help people build their marriages and families? Here are some practical ways you can make a difference in families today:

- Gather a group of couples and lead them through this study. Consider challenging others to form additional groups by doing another small-group study in the Art of Marriage Connect Series.
- Host the Art of Marriage video event or the Art of Marriage small-group series in your church or community.
- Consider using the *JESUS* film as an outreach. For more information contact FamilyLife at the phone number or website given on the next page.

- Host a dinner party. Invite families from your neighborhood to your home, and as a couple, share your faith in Christ.
- If you have attended FamilyLife's Weekend to Remember marriage getaway, consider offering to assist your pastor in counseling engaged couples, using the material you received.

For more information about these ministry opportunities, contact your local church or

FamilyLife
PO Box 7111
Little Rock, AR 72223
1-800-FL-TODAY
FamilyLife.com

our problems, God's answers

Every couple has to deal with problems in marriage—communication problems, money problems, difficulties with sexual intimacy, and more. Learning how to handle these issues is important to cultivating a strong and loving relationship.

The Big Problem

One basic problem is at the heart of every other problem in marriage, and it's too big for any person to deal with on his or her own. The problem is separation from God. If you want to experience life and marriage the way they were designed to be, you need a vital relationship with the God who created you.

But sin separates us from God. Some try to deal with sin by working hard to become better people. They may read books on how to control anger, or they may resolve to stop cheating or lying, but in their hearts they know—we all know—that the sin problem runs much deeper than bad habits and will take more than our best behavior to overcome it. In reality, we have rebelled against God. We have ignored Him and have decided to run our lives in a way that makes sense to us, thinking that our ideas and plans are better than His.

For all have sinned and fall short of the glory of God. (Romans 3:23)

What does it mean to "fall short of the glory of God"? It means that none of us have trusted and treasured God the way we should. We have sought to satisfy ourselves with other things and have treated them as more valuable than God. We have gone our own way. According to the Bible, we have to pay a penalty for our sin. We cannot simply do things the way we choose and hope it will be okay with God. Following our own plans leads to our destruction.

> There is a way that seems right to a man, but its end is the way to death. (Proverbs 14:12)

> For the wages of sin is death. (Romans 6:23)

The penalty for sin is that we are separated from God's love. God is holy, and we are sinful. No matter how hard we try, we cannot come up with some plan, like living a good life or even trying to do what the Bible says, and hope that we can avoid the penalty.

God's Solution to Sin

Thankfully, God has a way to solve our dilemma. He became a man through the person of Jesus Christ. Jesus lived a holy life in perfect obedience to God's plan. He also willingly died on a cross to pay our penalty for sin. Then He proved that He is more powerful than sin or death by rising from the dead. He alone has the power to overrule the penalty for our sin.

> Jesus said to him, "I am the way, and the truth, and the life. No one comes to the Father except through me." (John 14:6)

> But God shows his love for us in that while we were still sinners, Christ died for us. (Romans 5:8)

> For the wages of sin is death, but the free gift of God is eternal life in Christ Jesus our Lord. (Romans 6:23)

The death and resurrection of Jesus have fixed our sin problem. He has bridged the gap between God and us. He is calling us to come to Him and to give up our flawed plans for running our lives. He wants us to trust God and His plan.

Accepting God's Solution

If you recognize that you are separated from God, He is calling you to confess your sins. All of us have made messes of our lives, because we have stubbornly preferred our ideas and plans to His. As a result, we deserve to be cut off from God's love and His care for us. But God has promised that if we will acknowledge that we have rebelled against His plan, He will forgive us and fix our sin problem.

> But to all who did receive him, who believed in his name, he gave the right to become children of God. (John 1:12)

> For by grace you have been saved through faith. And this is not your own doing; it is the gift of God, not a result of works, so that no one may boast. (Ephesians 2:8–9)

When the Bible talks about receiving Christ, it means we acknowledge that we are sinners and that we can't fix the problem ourselves. It means we turn away from our sin. And it means we trust Christ to forgive our sins and to make us the kind of people He wants us to be. It's not enough to intellectually believe that Christ is the Son of God. We must trust in Him and His plan for our lives by faith, as an act of the will.

Are things right between you and God, with Him and His plan at the center of your life? Or is life spinning out of control as you seek to make your own way?

If you have been trying to make your own way, you can decide to change today. You can turn to Christ and allow Him to transform your life. All you need to do is talk to Him and tell Him what is stirring in your mind and in your heart. If you've never done this, consider taking the steps listed here:

- Do you agree that you need God? Tell Him.
- Have you made a mess of your life by following your own plan? Tell God.
- Do you want God to forgive you? Ask Him.
- Do you believe that Jesus' death on the cross and His resurrection from the dead gave Him the power to fix your sin problem and to grant you the free gift of eternal life? Tell God.

- Are you ready to acknowledge that God's plan for your life is better than any plan you could come up with? Tell Him.
- Do you agree that God has the right to be the Lord and Master of your life? Tell Him.

"Seek the LORD while he may be found; call upon him while he is near." (Isaiah 55:6)

Here is a suggested prayer:

Lord Jesus, I need You. Thank You for dying on the cross for my sins. I receive You as my Savior and Lord. Thank You for forgiving my sins and giving me eternal life. Make me the kind of person You want me to be.

The Christian Life

For the person who is a follower of Christ—a Christian—the penalty for sin is paid in full. But the effects of sin continue throughout our lives.

If we say we have no sin, we deceive ourselves, and the truth is not in us. (1 John 1:8)

For I do not do the good I want, but the evil I do not want is what I keep on doing. (Romans 7:19)

The effects of sin carry over into our marriages, as well. Even Christians struggle to maintain solid, God-honoring marriages. Most couples eventually realize they can't do it on their own. But with God's help, they can succeed.

leader's notes

about leading an art of marriage connect group

What is the leader's job?

Your role is more of a facilitator than a teacher. A teacher usually does most of the talking and instructing, whereas a facilitator encourages people to think and to discover what the Bible says. You should help group members feel comfortable, and keep the discussion moving forward.

Is there a structure to the sessions?

Yes, each session is composed of the following three sections. **Warm-Up** (5–10 minutes): The purpose of the Warm-Up is to help people unwind from a busy day and get to know one another better. Typically, the Warm-Up starts with an exercise that is fun but also introduces the topic of the session. **Master Designs** (45–50 minutes): This is the heart of the study when people answer questions related to the topic and look to God's Word for understanding. Some of the questions are to be discussed between spouses and others with the whole group. **Couple's Project** (60 minutes): This project is the unique application that couples will work on between the group meetings. Each project contains two sections: (1) On Your Own—questions for husbands and wives to answer individually and (2) With Your Spouse—an opportunity for couples to share their answers with each other and to make application in their lives and marriages.

What is the best setting and time schedule for this study?

This study is designed as a small-group, home Bible study. However, it can be adapted for more structured settings like a Sunday school class. Here are some suggestions for using this study in various settings:

In a small group

To create a friendly and comfortable atmosphere, we recommend you do this study in a home setting. In many cases, the couple that leads the study also serves as host, but sometimes involving another couple as host is a good idea. Choose the option you believe will work best for your group, taking into account factors such as the number of couples participating and the location.

Each session is designed as a sixty-minute study, but we recommend a ninety-minute block of time to allow for more relaxed conversation and refreshments. Be sure to keep in mind one of the cardinal rules of a small group: good groups start and end on time. Everyone's time is valuable, and your group will appreciate you respecting this.

In a Sunday school class

If you want to use the study in a class setting, you need to adapt it in two important ways: (1) You should focus on the content of the Master Designs section of each session. That is the heart of the session. (2) Many Sunday school classes use a teacher format instead of a small-group format. If this study is used in a class setting, the class should adapt to a small-group dynamic. This will involve an interactive, discussion-based format and may also require a class to break into multiple smaller groups.

What is the best size group?

We recommend from four to seven couples (including you and your spouse). If more people are interested than you can accommodate, consider asking someone to lead a second group. If you have a large group, you may find it beneficial to break into smaller subgroups on occasion.

This helps you cover the material in a timely fashion and allows for optimum interaction and participation within the group.

What about refreshments?

Many groups choose to serve refreshments, which helps create an environment of fellowship. If you plan to include refreshments, here are a couple of suggestions: (1) For the first session or two you should provide the refreshments. Then involve the group by having people sign up to bring them on later dates. (2) Consider starting your group with a short time of informal fellowship and refreshments (15–20 minutes). Then move into the study. If couples are late, they miss only the food and don't disrupt the study. (3) You may also want to have refreshments available again at the end of your meeting to encourage fellowship. But remember to respect the group members' time by ending the session on schedule and allowing anyone who needs to leave to do so gracefully.

What about child care?

Groups handle this differently, depending on their needs. Here are a couple of options you may want to consider:

- Have people be responsible for making their own arrangements.
- As a group, hire someone to provide child care and have all the children watched in one location.

What about prayer?

Prayer is an important part of a small group. However, as the leader, you need to be sensitive to people's comfort levels with praying in front of others. Never call on people to pray aloud unless you know they are comfortable doing this. You can take creative approaches, such as modeling prayer, calling for volunteers, and letting people state their prayers in the form of finishing a sentence. A prayer list can also be a helpful tool. You should lead the prayer time but allow other couples to create, update, and distribute prayer lists as their ministry to the group.

about the leader's notes

The sessions in this study can be easily led without a lot of preparation time; however, accompanying Leader's Notes have been provided to assist you when needed. The categories within the Leader's Notes are as follows:

objectives

The objectives focus on the issues that will be presented in each session.

notes and tips

This section provides general ideas, helps, and suggestions about the session. You may want to create a checklist of things to include in each session.

master designs commentary

This section contains notes that relate to the Master Designs questions, but not every question will have a commentary note. The number of the commentary note corresponds to the number of the question it relates to. (For example, the Leader's Notes, session 1, number 6 in the Master Designs Commentary section relates back to study session 1, Master Designs, question 6.)

Preventing Isolation

objectives

Guarding our hearts from selfishness is essential to a healthy and God-honoring marriage.

In this session couples will

- share enjoyable experiences from marriage,
- identify selfishness as the cause of isolation in marriage,
- affirm their awareness that God has a plan for preventing isolation in marriage, and
- choose a specific step to work on defeating selfishness.

notes and tips

1. If you have not already done so, you will want to read the information "About Leading an Art of Marriage Connect Group" and "About the Leader's Notes," starting on page 81.

2. As part of the first session, you may want to review with the group some ground rules (see page vi in Welcome to The Art of Marriage Connect).

3. At this first meeting collect the names, phone numbers, and e-mail addresses of the group members. You may want to make a list that you can copy and distribute to the entire group.

4. This first session contains a "Picture This" exercise that you can use as an additional Warm-Up activity if you desire. If you use this activity, be sure to watch your time so the session stays on track.

5. Because this is the first session, make a special point to tell the group about the importance of the couple's project. Encourage each couple to "make a date" for a time before the next meeting to complete the project. Mention that you will ask about this during Warm-Up at the next session.

6. You may want to offer a closing prayer instead of asking others to pray aloud. Many people are uncomfortable praying in front of others, and unless you already know your group well, it may be wise to venture slowly into various methods of prayer. Regardless of how you decide to close, you should serve as a model.

7. If there is room for more, you may want to remind the group that because this study is just underway, they can still invite another couple to join the group.

Master Designs Commentary

Here is some additional information about various Master Designs questions. (Note: The numbers below correspond to the Master Designs questions they relate to.) If you share any of these points, be sure to do so in a manner that does not stifle discussion by making yourself the authority with the real answers. Begin your comments by saying things like, "One thing I notice in this passage is . . ." or, "I think another reason for this is . . ."

3. Isaiah 53:6: "We have turned—every one—to his own way." Every person thinks primarily about himself, wanting his way first and foremost. This is selfishness.

5. Isolation can result in misunderstanding, pride, frustration, sexual and emotional dissatisfaction, and many other symptoms of a troubled marriage. (Note: If your group members have trouble coming up with effects of isolation, you may want to share these possible answers.)

6. Some people find overcoming isolation too difficult a task. Perhaps years of anger and resentment have left them feeling hopeless. Also, they may fear rejection from their spouses.

7. Mark 10:35–45 teaches a lifestyle of service and humility. These are the attitudes and actions of godly men and women. (This account is also told in Matthew 20:20–28.)

Developing Oneness

objectives

Oneness begins when both husband and wife build their marriage from the same set of designs: the Bible.

In this session couples will

- discover the benefits of oneness in marriage,
- identify commitment to God's designs as the key to achieving oneness and harmony in marriage,
- evaluate how God's designs for marriage are being followed in their homes, and
- plan specific ways in which to mirror God's image better in their marriages.

notes and tips

1. Session 1 raised concern over problems in a marriage. This session begins exploring God's designs for the solution to selfishness and isolation. Be sensitive to individuals or couples who struggle with accepting God's purposes as their own. Your warmth and acceptance can play a significant role in someone's decision to truly consider the principles of these sessions.

2. You may wish to have extra study guides and Bibles available for those who come to the session without them.

3. If someone joins the group for the first time in this session, give a brief summary of the main points of session 1. Also be sure to

introduce people who do not know each other. You may want to have each new couple answer the Warm-Up question from session 1.

4. If refreshments are planned for this session, make sure arrangements for them have been made.

5. If your group has decided to use a prayer list, make sure this is covered.

6. You will see a margin note with the Master Designs questions that suggests breaking into smaller subgroups if your group has a large number of people in it.

7. You may want to ask for a volunteer or two to close the session in prayer. Check ahead of time with a couple of people you think might be comfortable praying aloud.

master designs commentary

3. If your group needs help getting the discussion going, here are some possible answers you may want to share: by working hard at it, by improving your sex life, by each person taking his or her share of household responsibilities, and by working on the relationship.

4. Involving God in a relationship; obedience to God's Word.

5. Paul's instructions call for putting others' interests above our own. This is critical for achieving oneness in marriage.

7. Genesis 1:27: God made two distinctly different humans (male and female) so that together they would reflect the image of God.

Genesis 1:28: God created men and women as His ambassadors to glorify Him on earth and to tell others (friends, coworkers, neighbors) about the need to follow Christ.

Genesis 2:18: Companionship replaces isolation.

session three
Receiving Your Spouse

objectives

Oneness in marriage requires receiving your spouse as God's perfect provision for your needs.

In this session couples will

- identify the ways Adam needed Eve and compare those with ways they need their spouses,
- discuss the basis and the importance of receiving their spouses as God's perfect provision,
- analyze how weaknesses in their spouses have an impact on receiving them as God's provision, and
- affirm specific ways they and their spouses need each other and can accept each other as God's gift.

notes and tips

1. By the third session your group members should know one another well enough to feel somewhat relaxed and comfortable in talking—at least about the external aspects of their marriages. This session probes some very sensitive areas, exploring ways that we need our spouses. Some people may have difficulty admitting these ways to themselves or to their spouses, let alone to other people. Your role here—providing acceptance and support without pressing anyone—is crucial.

    Pray for sensitivity to each person as a unique being. And remind people that they can pass on any question they prefer not to answer.

2. A "Picture This" activity near the end of the Master Designs section calls for various household tools. If you plan to do this exercise, before the meeting you will need to gather an assortment of tools with opposing parts, such as pliers, scissors, tweezers, a manual can opener, and the like. Be prepared with at least one tool per couple.

3. The couple's project for this session involves writing a love letter. If some couples in your group have attended a FamilyLife Weekend to Remember marriage getaway, they may have previously done this exercise. If this is the case and it is brought up, ask the question: Can a person ever write too many love letters to his or her beloved?

4. Remember the importance of starting and ending on time.

5. You may want to make some notes right after the meeting to help evaluate how things went. Ask yourself questions such as, Did everyone participate? Is there anyone I should make a special effort to follow up with before the next session? Asking yourself questions like these will help you focus.

6. As a model to the group, you should complete the couple's project.

master designs commentary

2. What follows is how some commentators develop the meaning of Genesis 2:21–22. You may want to share these thoughts with your group.

   Caused Adam to sleep: Some people speculate that the sleep made the surgical procedure easier and kept Adam from offering unwanted advice about the woman's design.

Took a rib: This implies God recognized the equality of woman with man and depicts the strong emotional bonds between the sexes.

Closed the flesh: Adam was not harmed by this endeavor.

Made a woman: She was totally God's handiwork.

Brought her to Adam: God wanted Adam to recognize that the woman came from Him, that is, from God.

5. Obviously Eve was the only woman there, and we also can assume there was an immediate attraction between them. However, the only clue given in the passage is that Adam must have recognized that God was presenting her as a gift from Him. Adam trusted in the God who had created him and who had now provided a helper for him.

7. If the issue of spousal abuse is raised, call attention to these scriptures that provide wise counsel. Romans 13:1 and 1 Peter 2:13–15 teach God's establishment of governmental authority to control those who do wrong. A person in danger should not hesitate to contact the authorities for protection. Romans 5:8 shares Christ's example of loving the sinner even though hating sin (Psalm 45:7). One spouse's wrong acts do not excuse retaliation by the other. Proverbs 14:7 says to "stay away from a foolish man" (NIV). This does not mean divorce; it simply advises establishing enough space to avoid the influence of the fool.

8. Note: Rejection of the gift is rejection of the giver.
   It's possible someone may ask, "When we were married, neither of us even knew God, let alone trusted Him. How could my spouse be God's gift to me under that circumstance?" Refer the question to the group to answer. As you discuss this question, mention that the Scriptures clearly show that God is sovereign in the affairs of individuals and nations.

9. You can regard your spouse's weaknesses as opportunities for you to be needed and as God's tools to cause you to trust Him. Also, you should realize that some weaknesses will probably never be changed and those that are changed will occur only in a climate of loving acceptance.

Securing the Relationship

objectives

Building a strong and lasting marriage involves leaving parents, uniting with each other, and becoming one.

In this session couples will

- define the importance of leaving parents,
- discuss ways in which spouses unite with each other, and
- identify the connection between becoming one and achieving oneness.

notes and tips

1. Congratulations. With the completion of this session, you will be more than halfway through this study. It's time for a checkup: How are you feeling? How is the group going? What has worked well so far? What things might you consider changing as you head into the second portion?

2. One of the topics discussed in this session is leaving parents. On an issue like this, the focus can easily shift to a discussion about in-laws. While this may be interesting, it is not the point and should be avoided. If this happens, gently direct the discussion back toward the topic at hand by encouraging people to think in terms of their relationship with their own parents.

   Also, you may want to emphasize to the group that no longer being dependent on parents does not necessarily mean never receiving help or assistance from them. For example, a couple may borrow money from their parents. This transaction would probably not indicate dependence on the parents if it is handled in a courteous manner with an agreed-upon plan for repayment, which is then honored. Nor would parental help in a crisis necessarily indicate undue dependence. But a pattern of going to parents for repeated assistance is a danger signal.

3. You and your spouse may want to write notes of thanks and encouragement to the couples in your group this week. Thank them for their commitment and contribution, and let them know you are praying for them. (Make a point to pray for them as you write their note.)

4. By this time group members should be getting more comfortable with each other. For prayer at the end of this session, you may want to give anyone an opportunity to pray by asking the group to finish a sentence that starts something like this: *"Lord, I want to thank you for _____."* Be sensitive to those who are not comfortable doing this.

5. *Looking ahead:* For Master Designs in session 5, men and women will be in two different groups. For this part of the study, you will need a person to lead the group you're not in. Be sure to arrange for this prior to that session. Your spouse may be a good choice.

master designs commentary

3. When your parents are too clingy, you may not mature. Your spouse may develop resentments that will ultimately lead to conflicts.

   When you are dependent on parents and not on your husband or wife, your spouse is not allowed to meet your needs, thus thwarting oneness in your relationship.

4. Pray for your parents. Communicate with them regularly. Organize special events to honor them. Put together a special, written tribute to your parents. Care for them when your help is needed.

   If any couples in your group have parents who are elderly and becoming incapable of caring for themselves, you may want to ask, "How can a couple balance responsibilities to each other with the needs of aging parents?" (Although one's spouse must always be given first priority, that should not become an excuse to neglect responsibility to parents. See Mark 7:6–13 for Jesus' accusation against those who used their religious vows as an excuse to avoid caring for their parents.)

7. Physical union is an expression of oneness with the total person, uniting spirit, soul, and body.

9. This meant more than their physical nakedness. It also meant they were completely transparent with each other, feeling no threat in revealing themselves to each other.

Fitting Together

objectives

Husbands and wives have been given biblical responsibilities that complete rather than compete. When embraced, these lead to greater trust, peace, and security in marriage.

In this session couples will

- identify the biblical responsibilities husbands and wives have to each other,
- discuss things that interfere with fulfilling these responsibilities, and
- share ideas for encouraging each other to fulfill these responsibilities.

notes and tips

1. For this session the men and women will be in separate groups for Master Designs. Make sure you have asked someone to help facilitate the discussion for the group you are not in. You will also want to encourage that person to review the Master Designs Commentary notes related to the questions he or she will be responsible for leading.

2. If you choose to keep the men and women together for the Master Designs discussion, you will need either to (a) plan for additional time for the group discussion or (b) preselect which questions to discuss. You will not have time to cover them all in the normal amount of time.

3. In this session you will address a difficult and sometimes contro-versial topic—roles of husbands and wives. Many couples do not clearly understand what the Bible says about roles and will come in with preconceptions. You will want to challenge them to set aside their preconceived ideas—what they think or what the cul-ture thinks—and look at what the Bible says about these subjects.

4. Because of the subject matter, a group might spend a lot of time on one question. However, it is important for you as group leader to politely keep things moving forward.

5. As the leader of a small group, you can bless your group by pray-ing specifically for each member. Why not take some time to do this as you prepare for this session?

master designs commentary

Master Designs for Husbands

Note: In preparing for this session, be sure you have reviewed points 3 and 4 in the preceding Notes and Tips.

If some men begin to vent frustrations about their wives or about women in general, explain that the focus of this session is not on pointing out where their wives may be off base but on discovering ways they can become more successful as husbands.

2. Mark 10:42–45: Jesus clearly contrasted the self-important leader, who focuses on authority and status, with the servant-leader, who focuses on giving of self to the ones he leads. The servant-leader does not lord authority over others but willingly serves the needs of all. He does not demand service from others; rather, he gives up his own life and desires for others to have life—whether they deserve it or not.

3. If a man tends to be passive, it would mean taking his responsibilities seriously and beginning to initiate opportunities to serve his wife and meet her needs.

   A dictatorial husband would need to begin looking for ways to serve instead of to dominate. He would involve his wife in decisions and would be concerned with her fulfillment.

4. The husband loves and cares for the wife as Christ loves and cares for the church. Unselfish love is always demonstrated by giving of self, not just of things. Many wives have not seen their husbands deny themselves since courtship, and many others have never seen it at all. A husband's unselfish love frees the wife from her own selfishness and resentment, defeating isolation and building oneness.

Master Designs for Wives

Note: In preparing for this session, be sure you have reviewed points 3 and 4 in the preceding Notes and Tips.

Some women may want to vent frustrations about their husbands. Explain that the focus of this session will not be on pointing out where their husbands are off base but on discovering specific ways to become successful as wives.

16. The word *submission* comes from Greek words that mean "under" and "arrange." The sense of the term is to voluntarily organize or fit under.

    Submission does *not* require a wife to violate other scriptural commands or principles. The Bible does not ask wives to submit to sinful or damaging demands. If the issue of spousal abuse is raised, suggest these passages that provide wise counsel:

    Proverbs 14:7 says to "stay away from a foolish man" (NIV). This does not mean divorce; it simply advises creating enough space to avoid the influence of the fool.

Romans 13:1 and 1 Peter 2:13-15 teach God's establishment of governmental authority to control those who do wrong. A wife in danger should not hesitate to contact the authorities for protection.

Building in the Spirit

objectives

A husband and wife can experience true oneness only as they live by faith, in the power of the Holy Spirit.

In this session couples will

- contrast a marriage without God and a marriage with God,
- identify key elements necessary for walking with the Holy Spirit,
- discuss ways to restore and maintain a relationship with the Holy Spirit, and
- pray with everyone asking for God's power in their lives.

notes and tips

1. Realizing it is impossible to fully cover all the truth regarding the Holy Spirit in one session, the points covered here are intended to encourage individuals and couples to begin to experience the power of the Holy Spirit as an essential step in a lifelong process of Christian growth. For further study on this essential topic of Christian living, some excellent small-group studies are available from Cru.

2. Consider arranging for a group member—or your spouse—to share briefly about the Holy Spirit's ministry in his or her life and marriage. Meet with this person ahead of time to review what will be shared, making sure it will be brief, practical, and supportive of the concepts in this session.

3. If you sense that anyone in your group is not a Christian, this might be a good time to take a few moments to explain briefly how you can become a Christian and the differences that walking with Christ has made in your life. You can also refer group members to the article "Our Problems, God's Answers" in their books.

4. Encourage group members to do the exercise "For God's Eyes Only" on page 60.

5. To close the group meeting, you may want to pray the prayer found on page 56 aloud, or you may just want to allow time for silent prayer. After this time of prayer, you may choose to continue praying as a whole group or as couples. Another option would be to ask the question, "Does anyone have something they would like to share?"

6. Looking ahead: For the next session—the last session of this study—consider having someone, or a couple, from the group share what this study or the group has meant to them. If this is something you would like to do, be thinking about whom you might ask in advance to share.

master designs commentary

1. After hearing people's answer to this question, you could ask the follow-up question: "What stops us from carrying out our good intentions in our lives and marriages?"

4. The purposes for which God designed marriage cannot be achieved apart from His presence. The Holy Spirit is God's personal presence in your marriage. Intimacy with the Holy Spirit will release God's power in an individual and a marriage and will enable a couple to overcome the barriers to His purpose of oneness.

Shaping Your Legacy

objectives

The influence of your marriage will outlive you. What will the coming generations know about God because of your legacy?

In this session couples will

- compare a worldly legacy to a God-honoring legacy,
- identify the spiritual and physical legacies a marriage can leave,
- evaluate the direction of their lives and marriage and choose desired legacies to build, and
- discuss specific actions that can be taken to shape a God-honoring legacy.

notes and tips

1. It is crucial that you approach this seventh session as an opportunity to encourage couples to take specific steps beyond this series to keep their marriages growing. For example, you may want to challenge couples who have developed the habit of a date night during the course of this study to continue this practice.

   While this Art of Marriage Connect Series has great value in itself, gradually people will likely return to their previous patterns of living unless they commit to a plan for carrying on the progress made. Continuing effort is required for people to initiate and maintain new directions in their marriage. As one option this group might be interested in doing another study from this series.

2. If your group includes childless couples, emphasize spiritual descendants as well as physical descendants. Also, if there are couples whose children are grown or nearly grown and who are not serving Christ, encourage those parents that God is still able to overcome any mistakes made in earlier years. Encourage these parents to confess their errors to God—and to their children. This can be a powerful means of restoring relationships and communication.

3. As a part of this session, you may want to devote some time to planning one more meeting—a party to celebrate the completion of this study!

master designs commentary

4. Joshua 24:14–15: family commitment to fear and serve God

    Psalm 112:1–2: fear the Lord and delight in His commands

    Proverbs 22:6: intentional in training children

    2 Timothy 1:5: sincere faith

    3 John 4: walking in the truth

5. Matthew 28:19-20 instructs us to reach out to those in our world to make disciples. Second Timothy 2:2 stresses the importance of investing in faithful men, with the goal of helping them do the same with other faithful men.

6. A God-honoring legacy is obviously more than just physical reproduction. God's purpose is not just more people but people committed to God. Deuteronomy 6 shows that this is accomplished as parents tell and show God's truth to their children in the midst of everyday living.

more tools for leaders

Thank you for your efforts to help people develop their marriages and families using biblical principles. We recognize the influence that one person—or couple—can have on another, and we'd like to help you multiply your ministry.

FamilyLife is pleased to offer a wide range of resources in various formats. Visit us online at FamilyLife.com, where you will find information about our

- getaways and events, featuring Weekend to Remember, offered in cities throughout the United States;
- multimedia resources for small groups, churches, and community networking such as The Art of Marriage and Stepping Up
- interactive products for parents, couples, small-group leaders, and one-to-one mentors; and
- blogs, forums, and other online connections.

God can turn **any marriage** into a **masterpiece.**

Making marriage work is a divinely inspired art form. The Art of Marriage® video event incorporates expert teaching, engaging stories, real-life testimonies, humorous vignettes, and projects for couples in an expanded video-based format. Crafted with church or community settings in mind, this one-and-a-half-day event casts a compelling vision for marriage as God designed.

FAMILYLIFE® presents

the art of ♥ marriage®
a six-session video event

To learn more, visit
TheArtofMarriage.com

also available in **Spanish**

The Art of Marriage® small-group series

Over 350,000 have experienced stronger marriages as a result of The Art of Marriage video event. Now the same great content is available in a format perfect for Sunday school groups, home Bible study groups or any other small-group setting. In six sessions, we weave together expert teaching, real-life stories and man-on-the-street interviews to portray the hope and beauty of God's design for marriage.

The Art of Marriage small-group series kit includes:

- One DVD featuring six 20–25 minute video sessions

- A leader's guide

- Two workbooks that include small-group discussion questions, date night suggestions for couples, articles and more.

FAMILYLIFE® presents

To learn more visit
ShopFamilyLife.com

I, GREG,

PROMISE TO YOU, SHEILA, THAT I WILL PUT OUR MARRIAGE BEFORE WORK. NO MORE TEXTING YOU GOOD NIGHT FROM THE OFFICE OR SPENDING OUR VACATION AT THE REGIONAL SALES MEETING.

ABOUT FAMILYLIFE®

FamilyLife is a donor-supported nonprofit ministry headquartered in Little Rock, Arkansas, whose mission is to develop godly marriages and families who change the world one home at a time. Cofounded in 1976 by Dennis and Barbara Rainey, FamilyLife has strengthened millions of marriages and families through numerous resources, including:

- ▶ Weekend to Remember® marriage getaways
- ▶ *FamilyLife Today®* and *Real FamilyLife® with Dennis Rainey* radio broadcasts
- ▶ The Art of Marriage® Connect group studies for couples
- ▶ The Art of Marriage® video event and video series
- ▶ Stepping Up® video event and video series (for men)
- ▶ Passport2Purity®
- ▶ FamilyLife.com
- ▶ Hope for Orphans®

FamilyLife works in more than one hundred countries around the world and utilizes a volunteer network of more than twenty thousand people. They help bring God's message to others through the practical application of time-tested techniques and teachings that are based on biblical principles.

Find us online for more information.

 FamilyLife.com

 facebook.com/familylifeministry

@FamilyLifeOrg

notes

_____
_____
_____
_____
_____
_____
_____
_____
_____
_____
_____
_____
_____
_____
_____
_____
_____
_____
_____
_____
_____
_____
_____
_____
_____
_____
_____